un maglione

C'è un maglione.

There is one jumper.

Due

un gatto

Ci sono due gatti.

There are two cats.

Contents

Uno

un cane

C'è un cane.

There is one dog.

una scarpa

Ci sono due scarpe.

There are two shoes.

Tre

una ragazza

Ci sono tre ragazze.

There are three girls.

una sedia

Ci sono tre sedie.

There are three chairs.

Quattro

un uccello

Ci sono quattro uccelli.

There are four birds.

un cuscino

Ci sono quattro cuscini.

There are four cushions.

Cinque

un giocattolo

Ci sono cinque giocattoli.

There are five toys.

un libro

Ci sono cinque libri.

There are five books.

Sei

un cappotto

Ci sono sei cappotti.

There are six coats.

una matita

Ci sono sei matite.

There are six pencils.

Sette

una arancia

Ci sono sette arance.

There are seven oranges.

un biscotto

Ci sono sette biscotti.

There are seven biscuits.

Otto

una macchina

Ci sono otto macchine.

There are eight cars.

un cappello

Ci sono otto cappelli.

There are eight hats.

Nove

un palloncino

Ci sono nove palloncini.

There are nine balloons.

una candela

Ci sono nove candele.

There are nine candles.

Dieci

una mela

Ci sono dieci mele.

There are ten apples.

un fiore

Ci sono dieci fiori.

There are ten flowers.

Dictionary

See words in the "How to say it" columns for a rough guide to pronunciations.

Italian word	How to say it	English word
arancia / arance	ar-ran-chah / ar-ran-cheh	orange / oranges
biscotto / biscotti	biss-cott-oh / biss-cott-ee	biscuit / biscuits
c'è	cheh	there is
candela / candele	kan-deh-lah / kan-deh-leh	candle / candles
cane	kann-eh	dog
cappello / cappelli	kap-ell-oh / kap-ell-ee	hat / hats
cappotto / cappotti	ka-pott-oh / ka-pott-ee	coat / coats
ci sono	chee sonn-oh	there are
cinque	chin-kway	five
cuscino / cuscini	koo-shee-no / koo-shee-nee	cushion / cushions
dieci	dee-eh-chee	ten
due	doo-eh	two
fiore / fiori	fee-o-reh / fee-o-ree	flower / flowers
gatto / gatti	gatt-oh / gatt-ee	cat / cats
giocattolo / giocattoli	jo-kat-tow-loh / jo-kat-tow-lee	toy / toys
libro / libri	lee-broh / lee-bree	book / books
macchina / macchine	mak-kina / mak-kin-eh	car / cars

Italian word	How to say it	English word
maglione	mall-ee-own-eh	jumper
matita / matite	matt-ee-tah / matt-ee-teh	pencil / pencils
mela / mele	may-lar / may-leh	apple / apples
nove	no-veh	nine
otto	ot-toh	eight
palloncino / palloncini	pall-on-chee-noh / pall-on-chee-nee	balloon / balloons
quattro	qwa-troh	four
ragazza / ragazze	ragg-at-sa / ragg-at-seh	girl / girls
scarpa / scarpe	skarr-pah / skarr-peh	shoe / shoes
sedia / sedie	seh-dee-ah / seh-dee-eh	chair / chairs
sei	saee	six
sette	sett-eh	seven
tre	treh	three
uccello / uccelli	oo-chel-oh / oo-chel-ee	bird / birds
un / una	oo-n / oo-nah	a
un / una / uno	oo-n / oo-nah / oo-noh	one

Index

Notes for parents and teachers

In Italian, nouns are either masculine or feminine. The word for "a" or "one" changes accordingly – either un (masculine) or una (feminine). "Uno" is used when you write the number one on its own rather than as part of a sentence.